Audition Songs
Male & Female Singers
Christmas Ballads

Nine seasonal favourites
ideal for auditions

Audition Songs for Male & Female Singers
Christmas Ballads

Nine seasonal favourites
ideal for auditions

Wise Publications
part of The Music Sales Group
London/New York/Paris/Sydney/Copenhagen/Berlin/Madrid/Tokyo

Published by
Wise Publications

Exclusive Distributors:
Music Sales Limited
8/9 Frith Street,
London W1D 3JB, England.
Music Sales Pty Limited
120 Rothschild Avenue,
Rosebery, NSW 2018,
Australia.

Order No. AM85465
ISBN 0-7119-2724-3

Compiled by Lucy Holliday.
Music arranged by Derek Jones.
Music processed by Paul Ewers Music Design.

CD recorded, mixed and mastered by Jonas Persson.
Backing tracks arranged by Danny G. and John Maul.
Backing vocals by Elly Barnes.

Cover photograph (Frank Sinatra) by Brian Rasic courtesy of Rex Features.

Printed in the United Kingdom

Baby, It's Cold Outside

Words & Music by Frank Loesser

Dm7
G
C
G
C6
C/G
cold out - side.
Been hop - ing that you'd drop in.
cold out - side.
How luck - y that you dropped in.
This eve - ning has been so ve - ry
The wel - come has been so nice and
C9
F6
2fr
I'll hold your hands, they're just like ice.
Look out the win - dow at the stars.
nice.
My mo - ther will start to
warm.
My sis - ter will be sus -
F9
Beau - ti - ful, what's your hurry?
Lis - ten to the fire - place
Gosh, your lips look de - li - cious.
Waves up - on a tro - pi - cal shore -
wor - ry, my fa - ther will be pac - ing the floor.
So
-pi - cious, my bro - ther will be there at the door.
My

C6
D9
4fr
roar. Beau - ti - ful, please don't hur - ry. Put
line. Gosh your lips are de - li - cious.
real - ly I'd bet - ter scur - ry, or may - be just a half a drink
maid - en aunt's mind is vi - cious, or may - be just a ci - gar - ette
G7
C
G6
C6
G6
some re - cords on while I pour. But ba - by it's bad out there.
Nev - er such a bliz - zard be - fore. But ba - by you'd freeze out there.
more. The neigh - bours might think, say,
more. I've got - ta get home, say,
Dm7
G
Dm7
G
C
G6
No cabs to be had out there. Your eyes are like
It's up to your knees out there. I thrill when you
what's in this drink? I wish I knew how
lend me a comb. You've real - ly been grand

C6
C/G
C9
star - light now.
I'll take your hat, your hair looks
touch my hand.
How can you do this thing to
to break this spell,
I
but don't you see?
There's
3
F6
2fr
Am7(♭5)/E♭
D7
swell.
Mind if I move in clos - er?
What's
me?
Think of my life long sor - row,
if
ought to say no, no, no, sir.
At least I'm gon - na say that I tried.
bound to be talk to - mor - row,
at least there will be plen - ty im - plied.
G7sus4
G7
C
B♭6
A7
the sense of hurt - ing my pride.
Oh, ba - by don't hold out.
Ba - by, it's cold
you caught pneu - mo - nia and died.
Get ov - er that old out.
Ba - by it's cold,
I real - ly can't stay,
ah, but it's cold
I real - ly can't stay,
ba - by it's cold,

1.
D7
G7
A6
Em7
Fmaj9
out - side.
out - side.
Dm7
B♭maj9
G7
2.
D9
4fr
2. I
G7
C
N.C.
C13♯11
ba - by it's cold out - side.
ba - by it's cold out - side.

Blue Christmas

Words & Music by Billy Hayes & Jay Johnson

1.
2.
E7
A
5fr
A♭
4fr
G
3fr
F♯7
B
F♯7
A♯7
B7
N.C.
A
B♭dim7
B
B7
E
B7
- tions of red on a green Christ-mas tree,
- in' al-right with your
won't be the same dear, if you're not here with me. 2. And when the
Christ - mas of white. But I'll have a blue,
blue, blue, blue Christ-mas. Ooh,

E
B7
ah, ah, ah, ooh. Ooh,
E
ah, ah, ah, ooh. You'll be
E7
A
B♭dim7
do - in' al - right with your Christ - mas of white. But
B
B7
E7
A7
E
I'll have a blue, blue, blue, blue Christ - mas.

C.H.R.I.S.T.M.A.S.

Words & Music by Jenny Lou Carson & Eddy Arnold

F7
B♭
F7
I'd be get - ting lots of toys that day.
I learned a whole lot dif - f'rent when
B♭
C7
3fr
rit.
Mo - ther sat me down and taught me to spell Christ - mas this
F7
♩ = 88
B♭
way:
C is for the
E♭
6fr
Christ - child,
born up - on this day.

B♭
F
F9
H for her - ald an - gels in the night.
B♭
R means our Re - deem - er,
E♭
6fr
F9
I means Is - ra - el.
S is for the
B♭
star that shone so bright.

F7
B♭
T is for three wise - men, they who trav - elled
far.
C/E
C7
3fr
rall.
F7
M is for the man - ger where He lay.
B♭
a tempo
3
A is for all He stands for,
E♭
6fr
F7
S means shep - herds came and that's why there's a

B♭
Christ - mas day.
B
E
F♯7
rit.
And that's why there's a Christ - mas
3
B
E
B
day.

The Christmas Song
(Chestnuts Roasting On An Open Fire)

Words & Music by Mel Torme & Robert Wells

A tempo ♩ = 56
D♭ A♭6/E♭ Fm7 G♭maj7 A♭ D♭6/9 A♭m7 D♭9
Chest - nuts roast - ing on an op - en fire, Jack Frost nip - ping at your
G♭maj7 D♭11♯9 Faug♭9 B♭m F7aug♯9 D♭maj9 G♭m7 Cm7
nose. Yule - tide car - ols be - ing sung by a choir and
Fmaj7 F♯m9 B7 Emaj7 E♭9sus4 A♭7
folks dressed up like Es - ki - mos. Ev - 'ry - bo - dy
D♭add9 A♭7/E♭ Fm7 G♭maj7 A♭ D♭6/9 D♭7♯11
knows a tur - key and some mis - tle - toe, help to make the sea - son

G♭maj7
C7♭9
F7aug
B♭m
C♭7/G♭
bright.
Ti - ny lit - tle tots with their
D♭maj9
Gm9
3fr
C13
2fr
Fm7
B♭7
E♭m7
6fr
A♭7
4fr
eyes all a - glow will find it hard to sleep to -
D♭maj7
4fr
D♭
N.C.
A♭m7
4fr
D♭9
5fr
- night. They know that San - - - ta's on his
A♭m7
4fr
D♭9
A♭m7
4fr
D♭9
way, he's load - ed lots of toys and good - ies on his

G♭maj9
F♯m7
B9
sleigh. And ev - 'ry moth - er's child is gon - na
Emaj7
B♭m7
E♭maj7♯11
5fr
3
3
spy to see if rein - deer real - ly know how to
A♭7
4fr
A♭7
4fr
D♭6
3fr
G♭7♯11
fly. So I'm of - fer - ing this
Fm7
B♭7♭9
E♭m7
E/D
D♭9
G♭maj7
C7♯9
F7♭9
sim - ple phrase to kids from one to nine - ty two, al -

B♭m B7/F♯ D♭maj7 C9 G♭13 Fm7 B♭m7 E♭m7 A♭7♭9
-though it's been said ma - ny times, ma - ny ways, Mer - ry Christ - mas to
D♭6 N.C. D♭ E♭m7 D♭/F G♭
you. Love and joy come to you and to
B♭m7 A♭7 D♭ E♭/G♭ Fm7 B♭m7 E♭m7 A♭7
you your Christ - mas too, and God bless you and send you a
rit.
Fm B♭m E♭m7 A♭7 Fm7 B♭7 E♭m7 A♭7 D♭
Hap - py New Year. And God send you a Hap - py New Year.

The Christmas Waltz

Words by Sammy Cahn
Music by Jule Styne

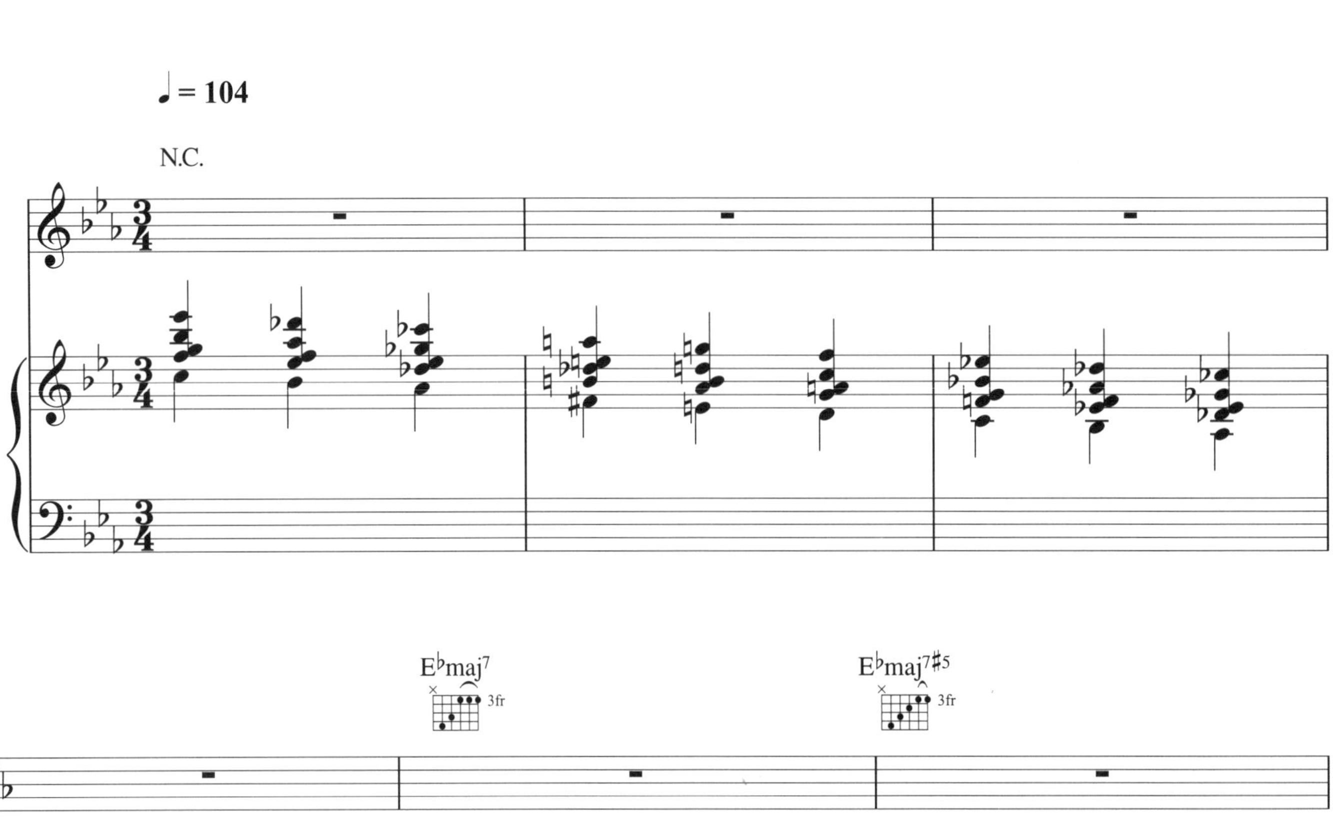

Fm7
B♭9
candles gleaming inside. Painted
E♭maj7
C7♭9
Fm9
candy canes on the tree.
B♭7♭9
E♭6
Santa's on his way, he's
Fm7
B♭7
Gm9
3fr
filled his sleigh with things,

Cm11
8fr
G/F
8fr
A♭7/B♭
B♭9(♯5)
rit.
*
things for you and for me. It's that
a tempo
E♭maj9
C7♭9(♯5)
Fm9
time of year when the world falls in
B♭7♭9
E♭maj7
C7♭9
Fm7
love, ev - 'ry song you'll hear seems to say
B♭7♭9
E♭6
Cm7/B♭
A♭maj7
4fr
mer - ry Christ - - mas, may your New

B♭6/9
Gm7♭5
C7♭9
Fm9
Year dreams come true. And this song of mine

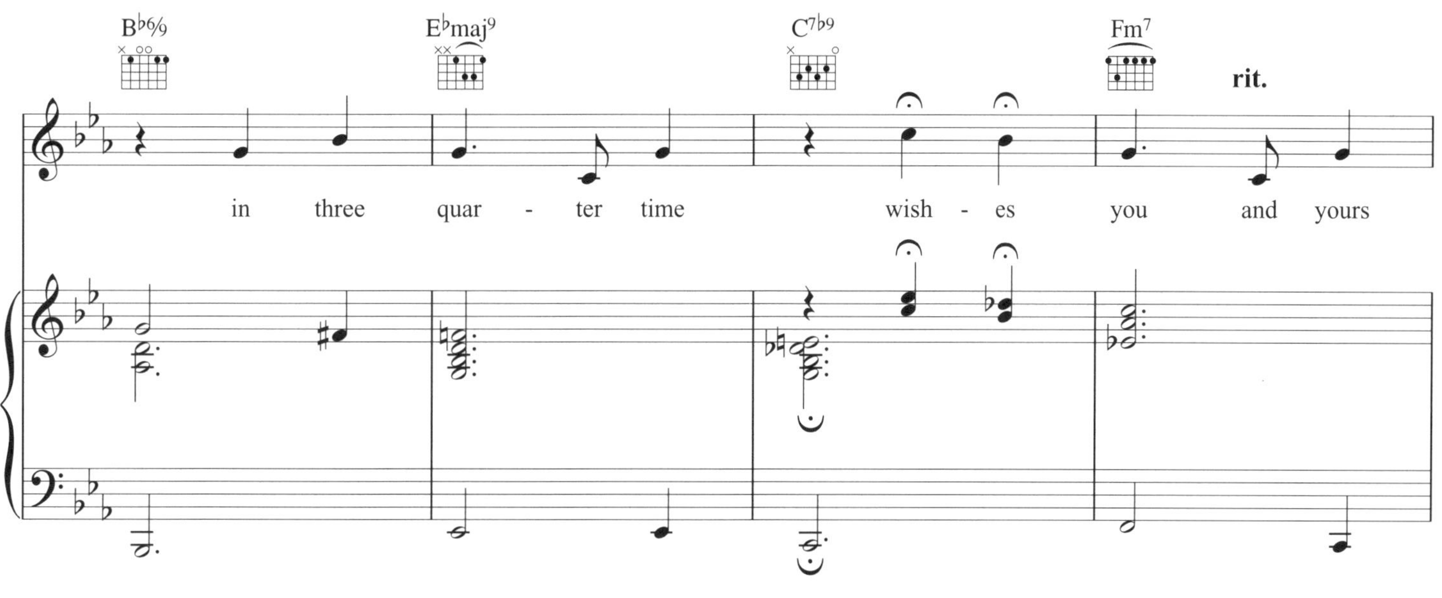
B♭6/9
E♭maj9
C7♭9
Fm7
rit.
in three quar - ter time wish - es you and yours

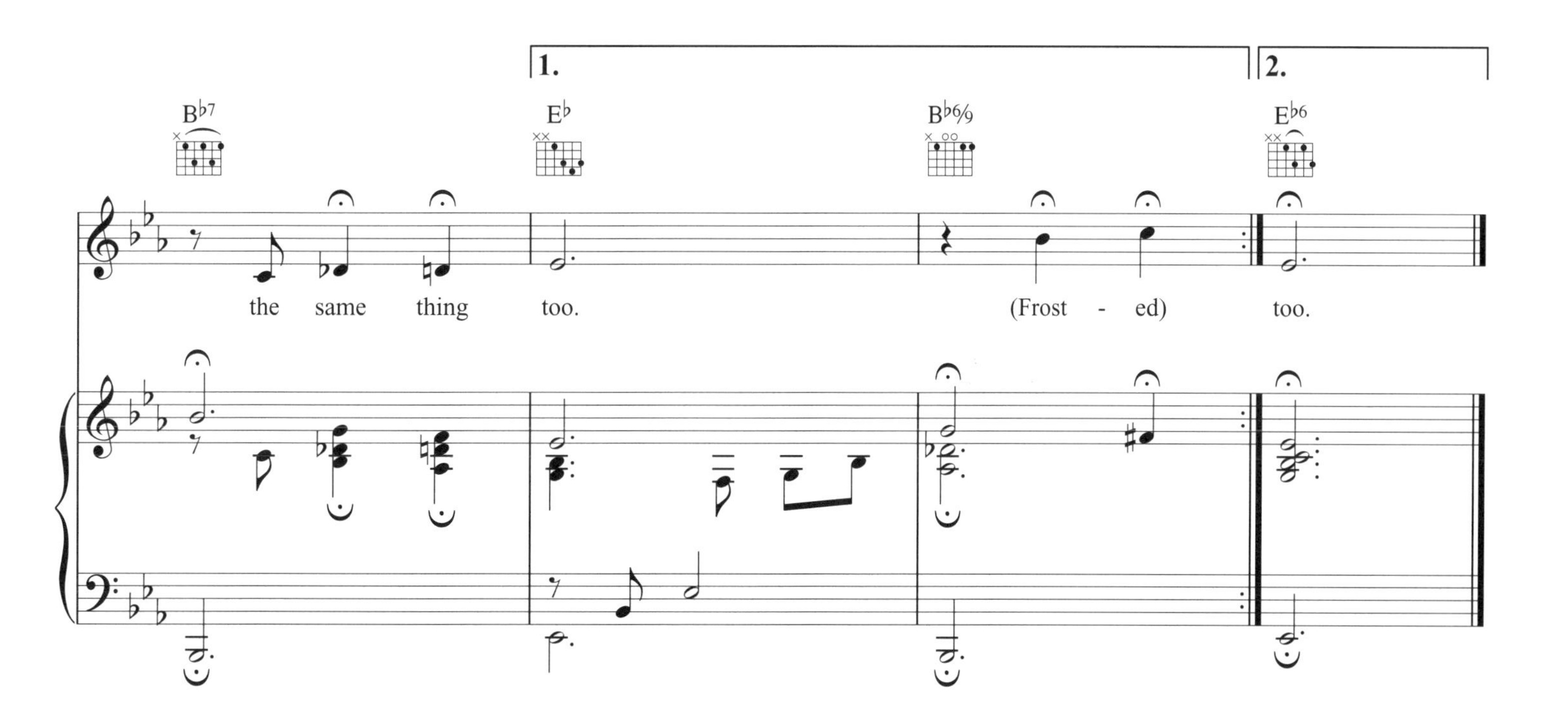
1.
2.
B♭7
E♭
B♭6/9
E♭6
the same thing too. (Frost - ed) too.

I Saw Mommy Kissing Santa Claus

Words & Music by Tommie Connor

Dm7
G7
Gmaj7+
C
B7
did - n't see me creep down the stairs to have a
C6/9
D7
peep. She thought that I was tucked up in my
G7
F/A
A7/C#
D7
G7
C
G/B
bed - room fast a - sleep.
Then I saw
And I saw
Am7
F#m7b5
F#maj7
Em7
A9
4fr
Dm7
G9
Mom - my tick - le San - ta Claus
Mom - my hug - ging San - ta Claus and

Gm9
C9
Gm9
C7
F
3fr
un - der - neath his beard so___ snow - y___ white.___
San - ta hugged her back right___ in plain___ sight.___
B7
What a laugh it would have been if
What a kick it would have been if
Em7
A7
Dm
C/G
F
C/E
E♭dim7
Dad - dy had on - ly seen Mom - my kiss - ing San - ta
Dad - dy had on - ly seen Mom - my kiss - ing San - ta
Dm7
G7♭9
1.
C
G/B
2.
C
E♭m7
A♭7
4fr
Claus last night. night.
Claus last

D♭6
Cdim7
B♭m7
G♭m7
Fm7
B♭7
E♭m7
A♭7
D6/9
Tap Dance
D♭6/9
Fm7
D♭6
B♭m6
A♭7
G♭13
F9
D♭/C♭
E7♭5
E♭m9
G7
A♭9
A♭9+
D♭6
C
D♭
B♭m7
E♭7
B♭7/D
D♭dim7
A♭/C
B♭m
A9
A♭6
N.C.
B♭6
Cm7♭5
Then

D♭
4fr
A♭/C
B♭m7
Gm7♭5
G♭maj7
Fm7
B♭9
E♭m7
A♭9
3fr
I saw Mom - my touch - ing San - ta Claus and
A♭m9
4fr
D♭7
4fr
A♭m9
4fr
D♭7
4fr
G♭
San - ta touched her back right in plain sight.
C7
3fr
What a hoot it would have been if
Fm7
B♭7
E♭m
D♭/A♭
G
D♭/F
E♭dim7
Dad - dy had on - ly seen…

E♭m7
A♭7♭9
D♭6
Dm/F
E♭m/G♭
F
It was a very strange night, I tell you, very strange!
G♭6
3fr
C7/G
5fr
C7♭9
Fm7
B♭7
E♭m7
6fr
Fm/A♭
4fr
G♭
Tap Dance
D♭/F
Edim7
E♭m7
A♭7
D♭/F
Edim7
E♭m7
A♭7
D♭/F
Edim7
E♭m7
A♭7
D♭
4fr
N.C.
Oh yeah!
8vb

Let It Snow! Let It Snow! Let It Snow!

Words by Sammy Cahn
Music by Jule Styne

Cm7 F9 B♭6 G7♭9 Cm7 F13♭9 B♭maj7 Cm7
3fr 4fr 3fr 3fr
let it snow, let it snow, let it snow. It does - n't show signs of
3
Dm7 E♭maj7 Dm7 C♯dim7 Cm7 Bdim7
5fr 6fr 5fr 5fr 3fr 3fr
stop - ping and I've bought some corn for pop - ping. The
Cm7 G7 Cm7 C♯dim7
3fr 3fr 3fr 5fr
lights are turned way down low, let it
Cm7 F9 B♭6
3fr
snow, let it snow, let it snow. When we
3

Fmaj7
C11
Fmaj7
F♯dim7
fi - nal - ly kiss good - night,
how you'll
2° Instrumental till *
Gm7
C7
Fmaj9
F6
Fmaj7
C11
hate go - ing out in the storm.
But if you real - ly hold me
Fmaj7
E7♭9♯11
E♭13♯11
D7♭9♯11
G9
C7
F11
F13
tight,
all the way home you'll be warm.
B♭maj7
Cm7
Dm7
E♭maj7
Dm7
C♯dim7
The fire is slow - ly dy - ing,
and dear, we're still good -

Cm7
Cm7
Bdim7
3fr
Cm7
G7
C♯dim7
5fr
-by - ing.
But as long as you love me so,
1.
F9
B♭6
let it snow, let it snow, let it snow.
2.
N.C.
let it snow, let it snow.
rit.
B♭maj7
Dm7
G7aug♭9
F7aug♭9
B♭maj9
Piano ad lib.

Santa Baby

Words & Music by Joan Javits, Phil Springer & Tony Springer

E♭m11
A♭13
D♭6
E♭7
A7
A♭7
hur - ry down the chim - ney to - night.
hur - ry down the chim - ney to - night.
(Ba, ba, ba,
D♭6
D♭/F
E♭7
A♭7
boom.) San - ta ba - by, a fif - ty four con - ver - ti - ble too, light blue.
San - ta cu - tie, and fill my stock - ing with a du - plex and cheques,
I'll wait up for you dear, San - ta ba - by, so
sign your x on the line, San - ta cu - tie, and
A9
hur - ry down the chim - ney to - night.
hur - ry down the chim - ney to - night.

F7
B♭7
Think of all the fun I've missed. Think of all the fel - las that I
Come and trim my Christ - mas tree, with some de - co - ra - tions bought at
E♭7
have - n't kissed. Next year I could be just as good if
Tif - fa - ny. I real - ly do be - lieve in you.
A♭6
N.C.
D♭6
D♭/F
you check off my Christ - mas list. (Ba boom, ba boom.) San - ta ba - by, I
Let's see if you be - lieve in me. (Ba boom, ba boom.) San - ta ba - by, for -
E♭7
A♭7
4fr
D♭6
D♭/F
want a yacht and real - ly that's not a lot.
- got to men - tion one lit - tle thing, a ring.

E♭7
A♭7
D♭6
D♭/F
Been an an - gel all year,
I don't mean on the phone,
San - ta ba - by, so
San - ta ba - by, so
1.
N.C.
hur - ry down the chim - ney to - night.
hur - ry down the chim - ney to - night.
D♭7♭5
4fr
2.
E♭m11
6fr
A♭13
Hur - ry down the chim - ney to - night.
Hur - ry, to - night.
D9
D♭

Home For The Holidays

Words & Music by Al Stillman & Robert Allen

A7
D7
G7
mat - ter how far a - way you roam, when you
C
F
F♯dim7
C
D7
pine for the sun - shine of a friend - ly gaze, for the
G7
F/A
B♭dim7
G7/B
C
C7
3fr
N.C.
ho - li - days you can't beat home, sweet home. I met a
*
F6
F
F♯dim7
man who lives in Ten - ne - see, and he was head - ing for

C
A7
G7
C
Pen - syl - va - nia and some home - made pump - kin pie.
C7
F6
From Pen - syl - va - nia folks are trav - 'lin' down to
F♯dim7
C
G
G♯dim7
Dix - ie's sun - ny shore, from At - lan - tic to Pa -
Am7
D7
G
N.C.
- ci - fic, gee, the traf - fic is ter - ri - fic. Oh, there's

C
F
C
no place like home for the ho - li - days
3
A7
'cause no mat - ter how far a - way you
3
D7
G7
C
roam, if you want to be
F
F♯dim7
C
D7
hap - py in a mil - lion ways, for the

G7
F/A
B♭dim7
G7/B
C
F
Gsus4
3fr
ho - li - days you can't beat home, sweet home.
1.
C
(Oh, there's)
2.
C
F♯dim7
G7
Dm7
For the ho - li - days you
Em/G
C♯dim7
3fr
F
G9
can't beat home, sweet
C6
home.

11/05(56920)

CD Track Listing

To remove your CD from the plastic sleeve, lift the small lip on the right to break the perforated flap.
Replace the disc after use for convenient storage.